MW01079522

If You Were
A Fish

*Produced by Daniel Weiss Associates, Inc.
27 West 20 Street, New York, NY 10011.*

*Copyright © 1989 Daniel Weiss Associates, Inc.,
and Al Jarnow.*

FIRST FACTS™ is a trademark of Daniel Weiss Associates, Inc.

*Published by Silver Press, a division of
Silver Burdett Press, Inc., Simon & Schuster, Inc.
Prentice Hall Bldg., Englewood Cliffs, NJ 07632
For information address: Silver Press.*

*Printed in the United States of America
10 9 8 7 6 5 4 3 2 1*

Library of Congress Cataloging-in-Publication Data

*Calder, S.J.
If you were a fish / S.J. Calder; illustrations by Cornelius Van Wright.
p. cm.—(First facts)
Summary: Introduces, in text and illustrations, the physical
characteristics, habits, and natural environment of the goldfish.
1. Fishes—Juvenile literature. [1. Goldfish. 2. Fishes.] I. Van Wright,
Cornelius, ill. II. Title. III. Series: First facts.
(Englewood Cliffs, N.J.)*

QL617.2.C35 1989   *89-6410*
597—dc20   *CIP*
                                            AC
ISBN 0-671-68602-X   ISBN 0-671-68596-1 (lib. bdg.)

First Facts™

If You Were
A Fish

Written by S. J. Calder
Illustrated by Cornelius Van Wright

Silver Press

Look at me swim!
I am a fish.
I have gills.
I have fins.
I have scales.

I am a goldfish.
You will not find me in the salty ocean.
I am a freshwater fish.
You will find me in a pond,
lake, river, or stream.

Have you ever seen me
in one of these places?

I started out as one of the tiny eggs
in a small cluster.

When I popped out of the egg,
I stuck to the first thing I touched.

As a baby goldfish, I was called a fry.
I had to feed and protect myself.
A yolk sac was attached to my body.
This is where my first food came from.

Now I find food for myself.
I gobble insects that skim the water.

I eat worms as they wiggle along the bottom.
I eat fish and water plants, too.

My whole life is spent in the water.
I breathe through my gills.
I swim by swinging my tail from side to side.
I use my fins for steering,
balancing, and stopping.

Watch me dart in and out of plants.
Watch me glide over rocks.
Watch me rest in the reeds.

My body is covered with scales that protect me.
Look at the shape of my scales.
Each one feels hard and smooth.
Yet they are thin and clear.

My scales grow as I get older.
A new ring appears on them every year.
If you count the rings on one of my scales,
you'll know how old I am.

You can see through my scales
to my beautiful gold skin.
Here are some other goldfish.

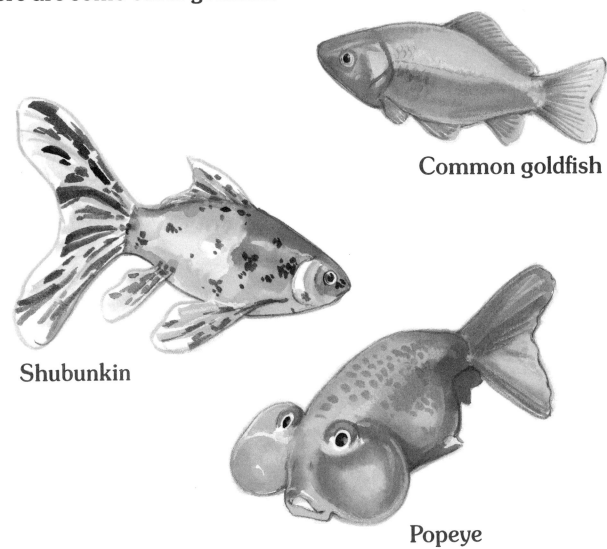

Common goldfish

Shubunkin

Popeye

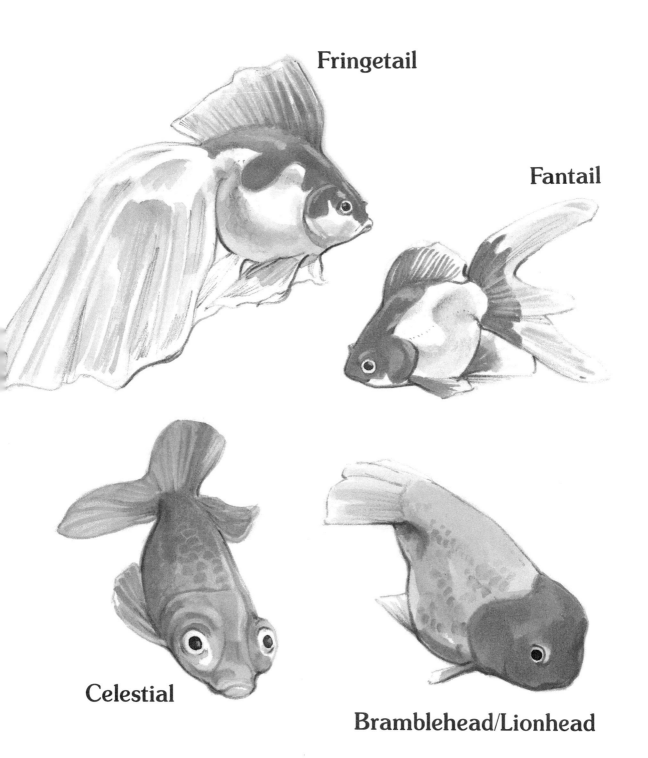

Fringetail

Fantail

Celestial

Bramblehead/Lionhead

My scales protect me from most things,
but not from my enemies:

Water snakes

Turtles

Water scorpions

Water beetles

Owls

Frogs

Other fish

Cats

They want to make a meal of me!

If there is danger near, I can see it.
I can see light, shadows, and colors.
My eyes are on either side of my head.
I have no eyelids,
because the water I live in
keeps my eyes moist and clean.

When I rest,
I go to the bottom of the pond
and stay completely still.

I wake up if I feel something
move in the water.

On each side of my body is a line
that goes from my head to my tail.
The line is made up of holes
that help me to feel vibrations.

When I swim from place to place,
I travel alone.

Other fish travel in schools.
A school of fish may be small . . .
or large.
I stay out of their way.

Not all fish live in ponds.
Many people make pets of goldfish.
You can have a goldfish for a pet, too.
Here's what you'll need to set up an aquarium:

1- a clean tank
2- plants to give off oxygen
3- gravel to hold plants in place
4- a tank light
5- a filter to keep the water clean
6- a snail to keep the tank clean
7- a castle for fish to dart through
8- fish food

In aquariums, goldfish are usually small.

But in the wild, goldfish are much bigger.
The pond gives us more room to grow.

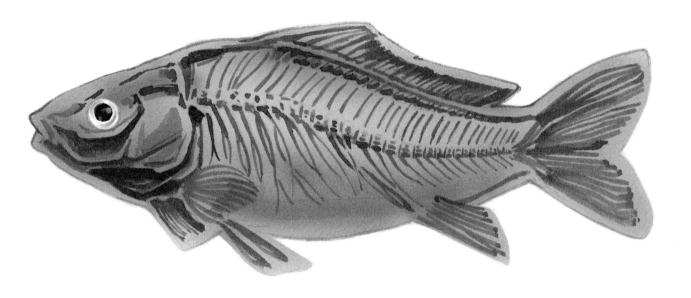

But no matter how big or small a fish is,
each one has a backbone.
And almost all fish have a skeleton.

Summer is the time of year when
I grow the most.
Food is plentiful.
The pond is full of life.

When winter comes, I hibernate.
I do not eat.
I stay still and hidden
at the bottom of the pond.
The water is warmest there.

As soon as spring comes,
I swim about again.

The next time you are near a
lake, river, stream, or pond,
look down in the water—
you'll see me swimming by.
There I go!